MW00396797

About the Legends of Africa Series

Every new generation of children should be enthralled by stories of famous people from their history. The Legends of Africa Series are fictionalized stories about real legends of Africa from the continent and the African diaspora. The stories are written in easy to read texts which can be read to young children. Older children will also enjoy them because they are easy to read and understand.

Published by Nurturingminds.com (Nana Daycare)
https://nanadaycare.org/
Bowmanville, Ontario, Canada
Copyright Bunmi Oyinsan 2020

All rights reserved. No part of this publication may be reproduced, stored in a retrieval system, or transmitted in any form or by any means, electronic, mechanical, photocopying, recording or otherwise, without the prior consent of the copyright owner.
This book is sold subject to the condition that it shall not by way of trade or otherwise, be lent, resold, hired out or otherwise circulated without the copyright owner's prior consent in any form of binding or cover other than that which it is published and without a similar condition including this condition being imposed on subsequent purchaser.

ISBN 978-1-7772182-2-5

1

Mansa Musa
The Richest Man Who Ever Lived

Written by Bunmi Oyinsan, PhD

Illustrated by Sardar Hammad Khan

Dedicated to my grandchildren

Once upon a time in West Africa, there was an empire called Mali which was flowing with treasure. The land was rich in copper, silver, gold, and salt. At that time in history, salt was as rare as any precious metal.

Mansa is the Mandika word for emperor or king. Before Mansa Musa was born, Mali was ruled by another Mansa called Mansa Bogari. Mansa Bogari's palace was large with hundreds of rooms.

5

Mansa Bogari had a sister who was a beautiful and strong willed woman. She fell in love and followed her heart by marrying a man who was not from the royal family. She moved out of the palace to live with her husband in a humble home not too far from the palace.

One day, she gave birth to a son and named him Musa. She raised him well, and Musa grew tall, dark and handsome, but he did not depend on his looks to get him through life.

With the help of his parents, Musa worked hard and was diligent at his lessons.

One day, Musa and his mother were summoned to Mansa Bogari's palace. The palace was beautiful and built out of timber, mahogany and ebony. The windows were decorated with the most beautiful corals and seashells. The floor was made out of marble and granite.

In the palace, Mansa Bogari was attended by hundreds of loyal servants who loved him because he was kind and generous. When they arrived at the palace, Mansa Bogari embraced his sister and nephew. He then told his sister that he had heard many good things about Musa.

"I want Musa to come and live here in the palace with me." He told Musa's mother. Musa moved to the Royal Palace, and Mansa Bogari taught him all there was to know about ruling an empire as rich and powerful as Mali.

Mansa Bogari was a restless man, and he was curious to know what lay beyond on the other side of the great Atlantic Ocean.

So he sent two hundred boats filled with two thousand sailors out to sea to find out what lay beyond the great ocean. He gave them bags and bags of gold, enough water and food to last them for several months.

Do not return till you reach the end of the Atlantic. Only then should you come back and tell me what you have seen," Mansa Bogari commanded the sailors.

The sailors sailed for days, weeks and months, but they did not get to the end of the Atlantic Ocean. The sailors turned back towards home when they ran out of food and water.

When they got back to Mali, they reported to Mansa Bogari. "Oh mighty Mansa. We sailed for days, weeks and months. All we found was the sea and more sea. Surely, there is no land beyond the sea."

13

Mansa Bogari was convinced that there had to be other lands beyond the sea, so he sent another group of sailors. He kept sending teams of sailors off to sea and was most unhappy when they all came back and told him that the Atlantic was so big, so deep and so wide that they sailed for many days, many weeks and many months and did not get to the end of it.

Unhappy with the sailors who kept coming back from exploring the sea without finding any other land, Mansa Bogari decided to set sail himself.

"Fill two thousand boats with water, food and treasures. I will set sail on a voyage to the end of the Atlantic Ocean myself!" he ordered his imperial servants.

He then ordered one thousand more boats to be loaded with treasures in case he found other countries and empires.

He was a generous man and he did not want to go visiting other lands without bearing gifts for the people he might meet.

On the day he set sail, thousands of his citizens came out to bid him farewell. Musa too was there. He had grown taller, more handsome and wiser.

He was at the sea port to see his uncle, Mansa Bogari off and he was very sad. Musa was feeling sad because he wanted his uncle to take him along. At the seaport, he hugged his uncle. "Please Uncle, take me with you!" Musa pleaded.

"Do not fret, young Musa. I'll be back with treasures for you from afar. Besides, my dear nephew, I'm leaving you in charge of all my empire. Take good care of it while I am gone. Yakub and Issa, my ministers, will assist you."

Several months after Mansa Bogari set sail, Musa and the people of Mali became worried. They hoped that their Mansa was safe and would return.

So Musa sent other sailors to go and look for him, but they returned with no news of their Mansa.

Again and again, Musa kept sending men to sea in search of his uncle.

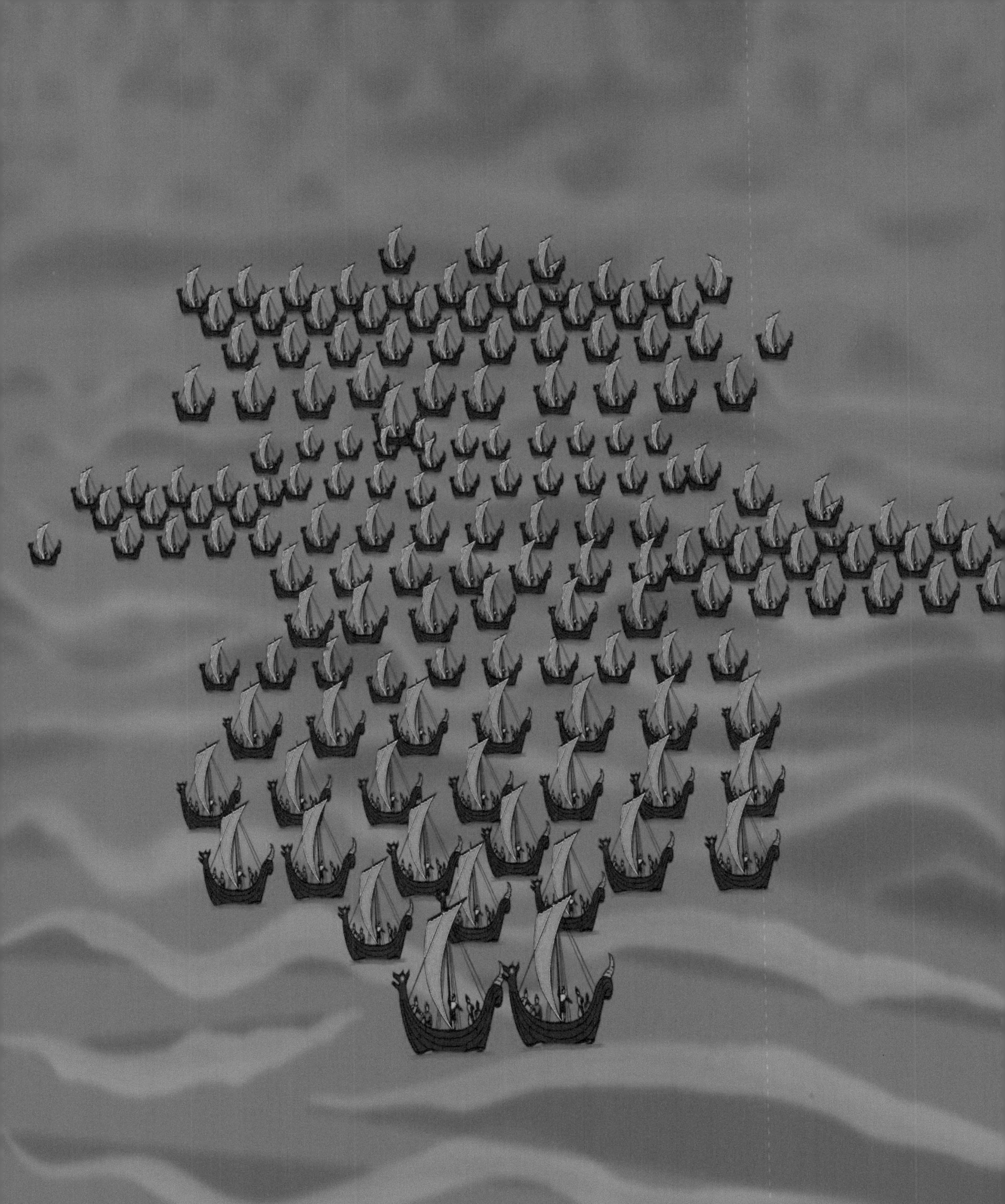

The people of Mali had no choice but to accept that Mansa Bogori had perished at sea.

They crowned Musa as the new Mansa since the late Mansa had appointed him to look after the empire in his absence. From the day of his coronation he became know as Mansa Musa.

Soon, Yakub and Issa, the old ministers decided to plot against Mansa Musa

"Now that Mansa Bogari is surely dead at sea, the empire is ours to wrest from young Musa's hands," said Issa to Yakub.

First, they tried to turn the citizens of Mali against Mansa Musa. They started a rumour saying that Mansa Musa wanted everyone in the empire to change to his religion.

This started a revolt among the citizens, but when news of the rumour got to Mansa Musa, he went from province to province proclaiming the rights of people to freedom of religion.

The citizens were pleased to see their Mansa taking such an impartial stand, and the revolts were quickly stopped.

Next, Issa and Yakub hatched another plot. They hired highway robbers to waylay merchants who came to trade in Mali.

When word of the robberies got to Mansa Musa, he sent an army of the finest horsemen in the realm to go and catch them.

He instructed the horsemen not to kill the robbers but to bring them back to him alive. Mansa Musa was wise and knew that if the robbers were captured alive, he would find out who was behind them.

His plan worked. The robbers confessed, and Mansa Musa banished the old unfaithful ministers from the land.

He then appointed several wise young men and put them in charge of the various provinces under his realm.

Mansa Musa's empire grew more prosperous. His miners mined more copper, silver, gold and salt than ever. From far and near, traders came to the markets in Mali. The empire was safe, and the people were happy.

Mansa Musa too was pleased that the empire was more prosperous than ever. He decided to go on a pilgrimage.

He wanted to go to lands far and near to find and bring back the best architects to help beatify his land. He also wanted to bring back scholars and scientists who would build schools, universities and other centers of learning in Mali.

Unlike his uncle the former Mansa, Musa did not to go by sea to find other lands. He decided instead to cross the Sahara Desert.

"Saddle up five hundred of the strongest camels in the land!" he ordered his imperial servants. "Load them up with food, water, gold and silver."

Mansa Musa and his Queen got ready for their journey. When their caravan was ready to embark on the pilgrimage, the people came out to behold the beauty and bounty of their land on display.

The camels were saddled with the most beautifully decorated leather. They were draped with the finest and most colourful textiles from the land.

There were hundreds of horses ridden by royal horsemen in the caravan. They were carrying the golden banners of the empire.

Mansa Musa visited Cairo in Egypt during his pilgrimage. Egypt, which at one time was the greatest empire in the world, had declined.

To help boost Egypt's economy, Mansa Musa spent much money and distributed so much gold in the city of Cairo that his fame soon spread all over the world.

32

His fame spread far and wide and all over Europe, news of this great ruler quickly spread. Mansa Musa was hailed as a great ruler and the richest man who ever lived.

Tales of the gold that Mansa Musa spent and gave out during this pilgrimage made explorers from other lands desperate to brave the Sahara Desert in search of Mansa Musa's golden empire.

He returned to Mali bringing back the best architects who designed the finest buildings and schools ever seen.

He also brought back great scholars
and scientists who helped him to
establish great schools, universities
and other centers of learning in the
city of Timbuktu. All these made the
Mali Empire richer and more famous.

CPSIA information can be obtained
at www.ICGtesting.com
Printed in the USA
BVHW020959050721
611158BV00013B/202

* 9 781777 218225 *